Anthony Josephson

The Happy Zoo

Bumblebee Books
London

A CIP catalogue record for this title is
available from the British Library.

ISBN: 978-1-83934-220-2

Bumblebee Books is an imprint of
Olympia Publishers.

First Published in 2021

Bumblebee Books
Tallis House
2 Tallis Street
London
EC4Y 0AB

Printed in Great Britain

www.olympiapublishers.com

Dedication

Thea and Margot, I hope one day you get to experience all the beauty of nature and the world in a way I've been lucky enough to. Love Daddy.

Welcome to The Happy Zoo,
Made for explorers just like you.
Come on in. There's lots to see.
Come meet the animals with me.

We've got many different animals
different types and different breeds.
Animals with different tastes,
different wants and different needs.

They range from frogs, fish and chinchillas
through to birds, lions and gorillas.

THE HAPPY ZOO GUIDE

Open the gates and here we go,
The Happy Zoo always puts on a good show.

First, look up towards the sky,
Where the birds are flying high.

The hornbill's there, with its bright yellow head.
The macaws are for you if you like red instead.
The owls hoot, the parrots squark.
That's just how our birds talk.

Crocodiles and alligators
are next for us to see.
They're big and powerful with
more teeth than you or me.

We have lizards, chameleons
and even dragons too.
Turtles, tortoises and snakes
complete the reptiles in our zoo.

The aquarium is next with the
fish and all their scales,
But we don't house any dolphins,
sharks or any whales.

The fish are brightly coloured,
small, big, spiky and round.
With all our tanks there are
many fish here to be found.

✓ BIG

✓ SMALL

✓ SPIKY

✓ ROUND

✓ COLOURFUL

Up next on our tour the
amphibians wait for you.
We've got lots of frogs and toads,
salamanders and newts too.

They can all breathe underwater,
and also on the land,
On grass and in the marshes
and even on the sand.

THE AMPHIBIAN ZONE

Our monkeys can be cheeky,
watch out for the food in your hand.
The orangutans and gorillas
are smart, they understand.
They're very much like people,
like you and like me.
With their numbers in decline
they're a sight we're lucky to see.

There's an elephant with his trunk
and a rhino with her horn.

Once very common in nature,
far fewer are now being born.

We've also got some big cats; cheetahs, lions and tigers to name a few.

For now our tour comes to an end.
There's nothing left to do.

Many of these animals may
not be around for long.
For many years man-kind
has treated their home wrong.

Look after their home, look after the Earth.
Keep it clean and value its worth.

If we all join together, love
and protect the wild,
You can talk about these animals
in years to come, with your child.
You can sit down and tell them
about The Happy Zoo.
"When I was a child,
I went there too."

About the Author

Anthony is an optometrist by career and has four children (two human, two canine). He has a passion for performing theatre and writing little stories and poems. *The Happy Zoo* is his first published work.

Printed in Great Britain
by Amazon